NEW CHART HITS
Playalong *for* Clarinet

Anyone Of Us (Stupid Mistake) 6
Gareth Gates

Colourblind 8
Darius

Complicated 11
Avril Lavigne

If You're Not The One 14
Daniel Bedingfield

I'm Gonna Getcha Good! 17
Shania Twain

Love At First Sight 20
Kylie Minogue

Round Round 23
Sugababes

The Tide Is High (Get The Feeling) 26
Atomic Kitten

Unbreakable 28
Westlife

Whenever, Wherever 30
Shakira

Clarinet Fingering Chart 3

Wise Publications
PART OF THE MUSIC SALES GROUP
London/New York/Paris/Sydney/Copenhagen/Berlin/Madrid/Tokyo

Published by:
Wise Publications
8/9 Frith Street, London W1D 3JB, England.

Exclusive Distributors:
Music Sales Limited
Distribution Centre, Newmarket Road, Bury St. Edmunds,
Suffolk IP33 3YB England.
Music Sales Pty Limited
120 Rothschild Avenue, Rosebery, NSW 2018, Australia.

Order No. AM963083
ISBN 0-7119-8068-3
This book © Copyright 2003 by Wise Publications.

Compiled by Nick Crispin.
Music arranged by Simon Lesley.
Music processed by Enigma Music Production Services.
Cover photography by George Taylor.
Printed in Great Britain.

CD recorded, mixed and mastered by Jonas Persson.
Backing tracks by Danny G.
Instrumental solos by John Whelan.

Your Guarantee of Quality:
As publishers, we strive to produce every book to
the highest commercial standards.
The music has been freshly engraved and the book has been
carefully designed to minimise awkward page turns and
to make playing from it a real pleasure.
Particular care has been given to specifying acid-free, neutral-sized
paper made from pulps which have not been elemental chlorine bleached.
This pulp is from farmed sustainable forests and was
produced with special regard for the environment.
Throughout, the printing and binding have been planned to
ensure a sturdy, attractive publication which should give years of enjoyment.
If your copy fails to meet our high standards,
please inform us and we will gladly replace it.

www.musicsales.com

Clarinet Fingering Chart

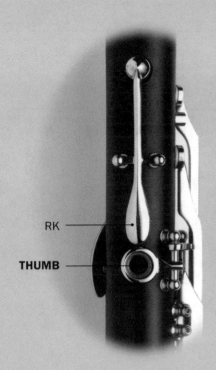

RK

THUMB

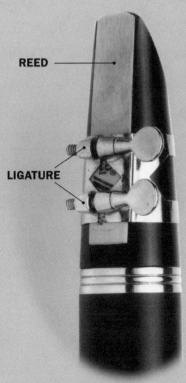

REED

LIGATURE

Mouthpiece

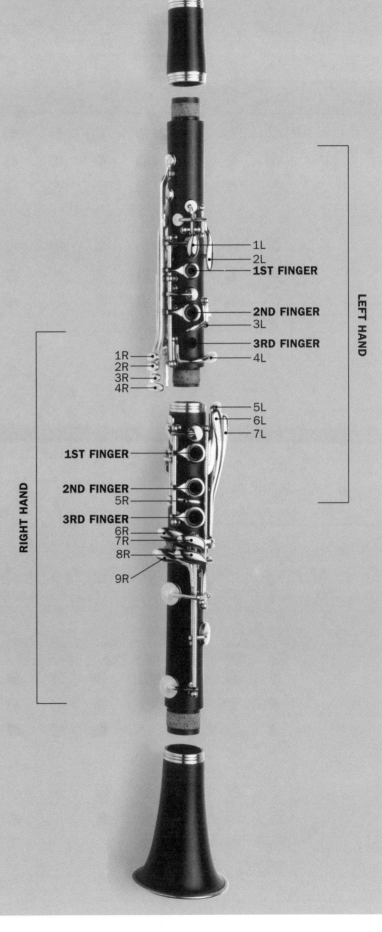

1L
2L
1ST FINGER

2ND FINGER
3L

3RD FINGER
4L

1R
2R
3R
4R

5L
6L
7L

1ST FINGER

2ND FINGER
5R

3RD FINGER
6R
7R
8R

9R

LEFT HAND

RIGHT HAND

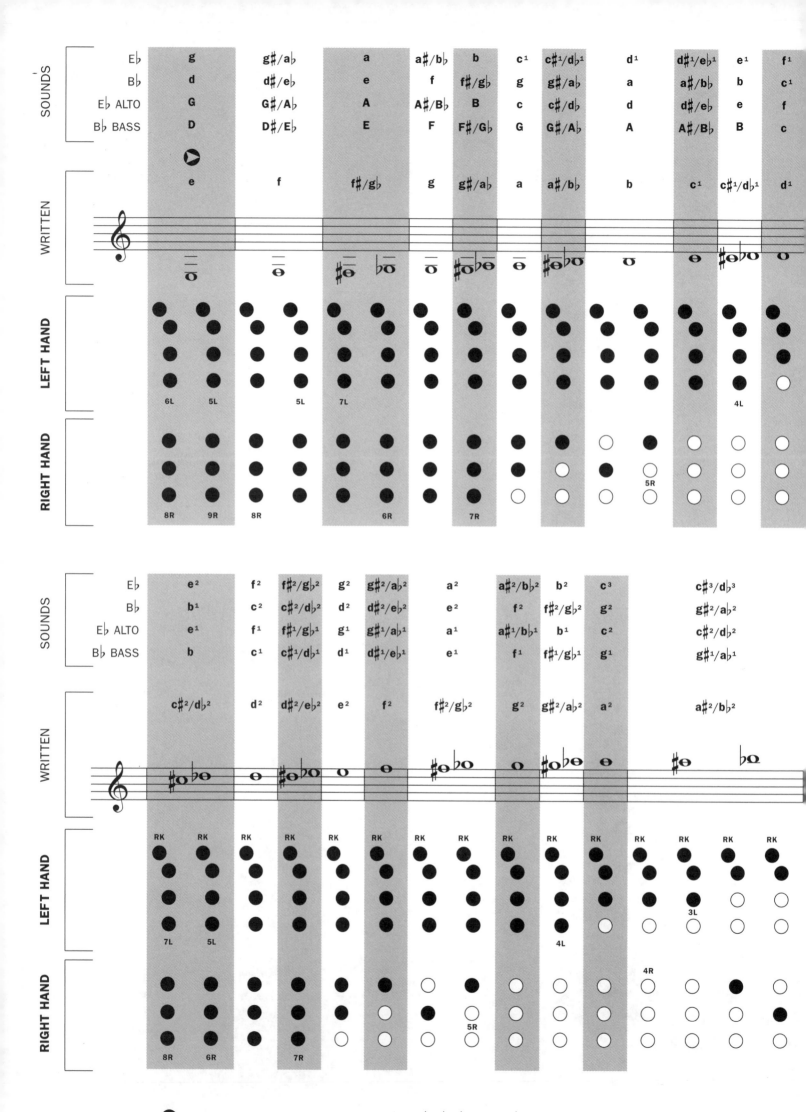

Indicates the lower limit of the best playing range for E♭, B♭, E♭ Alto and B♭ Bass Clarinets

Indicates the upper limit of the best playing range for E♭ and B♭ Clarinets

Indicates the upper limit of the best playing range for E♭ Alto and B♭ Bass Clarinets

Anyone Of Us (Stupid Mistake)

Words & Music by Jörgen Elofsson, Per Magnusson & David Kreuger

Colourblind

Words & Music by Darius, Pete Glenister & Denny Lew

9

Repeat to fade

10

Complicated

Words & Music by Lauren Christy, David Alspach, Graeme Edwards & Avril Lavigne

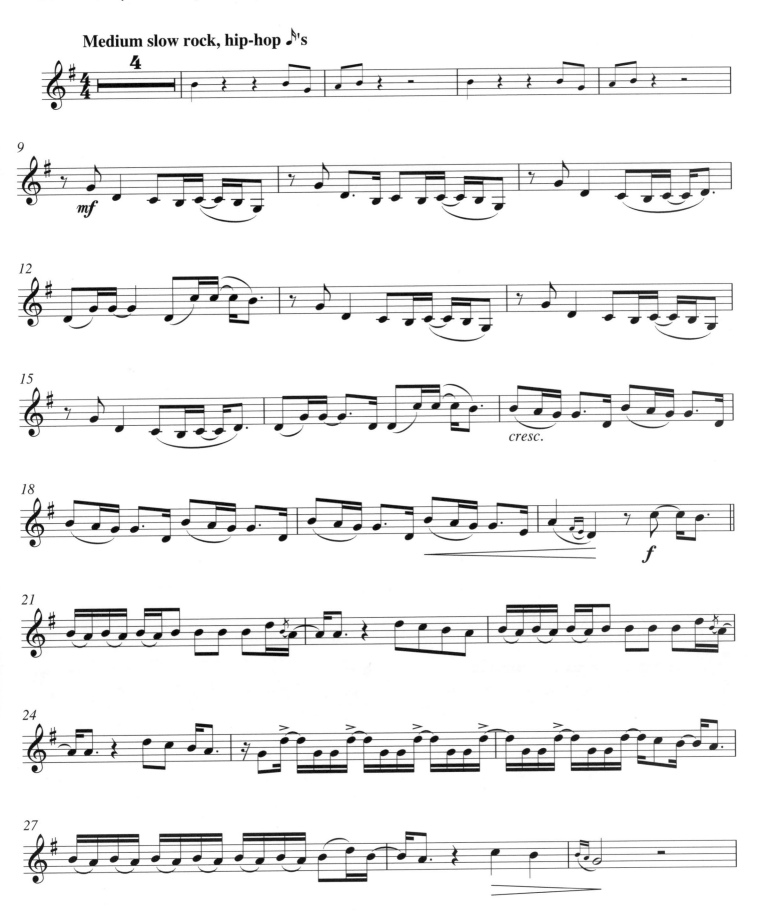

If You're Not The One

Words & Music by Daniel Bedingfield

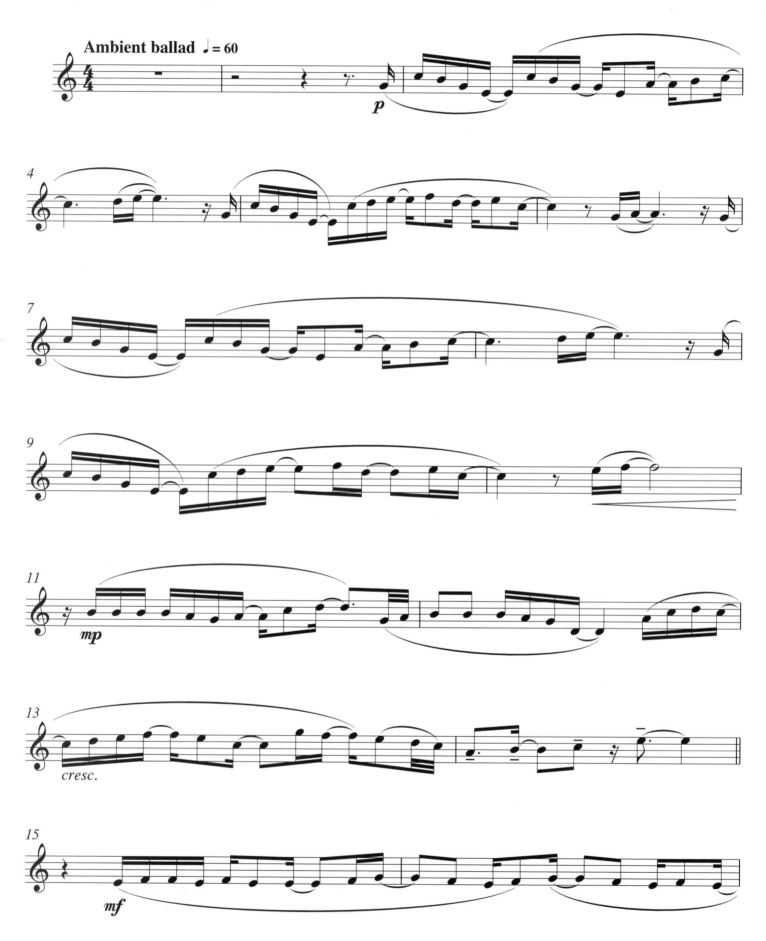

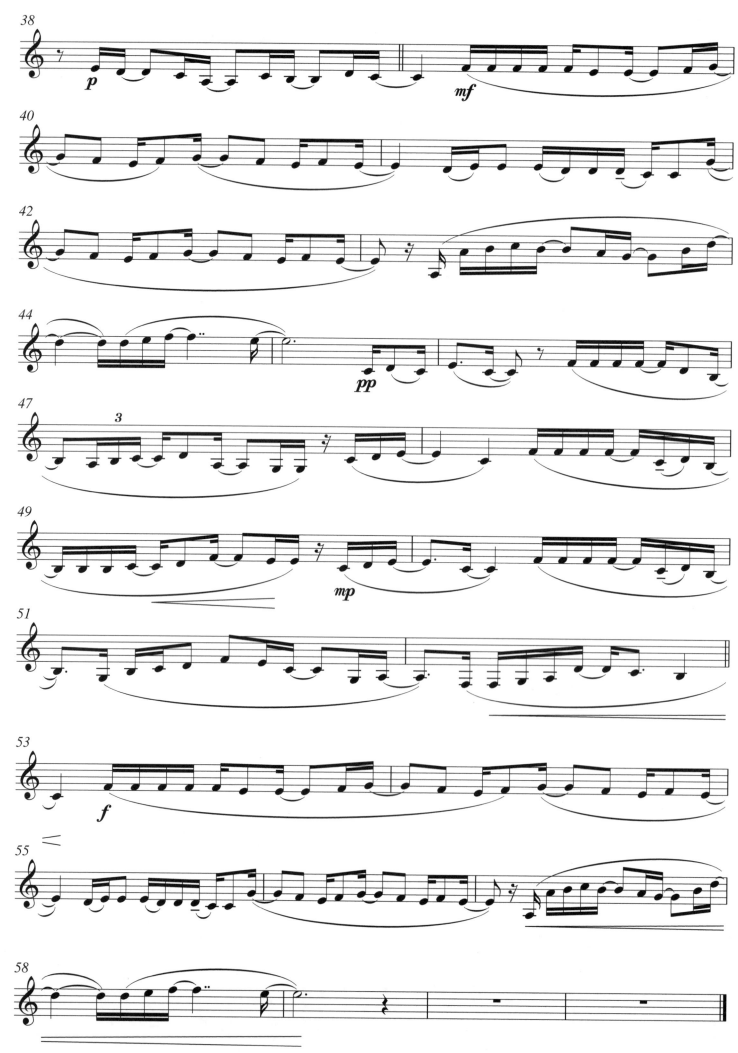

I'm Gonna Getcha Good!

Words & Music by Shania Twain & Robert John "Mutt" Lange

Line-dancing rock ♩ = 124

Love At First Sight

Words & Music by Kylie Minogue, Richard Stannard, Julian Gallagher, Ash Howes & Martin Harrington

Groove pop ♩ = 125

Round Round

Words & Music by Brian Higgins, Timothy Powell, Miranda Cooper, Felix Strecher, Robin Hoffman,
Rino Spadavecchia, Florian Pfleuger, Keisha Buchanan, Mutya Buena, Heidi Range, Nicholas Coler & Lisa Cowling

Tempo primo

The Tide Is High (Get The Feeling)

Words & Music by John Holt, Howard Barrett, Tyrone Evans, Bill Padley & Jem Godfrey

Unbreakable

Words & Music by Jorgen Elofsson & John Reid

Whenever, Wherever

Words by Shakira & Gloria Estefan
Music by Shakira & Tim Mitchell

quasi panpipes

rit.